SNOOPY STARS

—AS—
THE FEARLESS LEADER

Charles M. Schulz

ЯR
RAVETTE BOOKS

First published by
Ravette Books Limited 1988
Revised 1989

Printed and bound in Great Britain
for Ravette Books Limited,
3 Glenside Estate, Star Road, Partridge Green,
Horsham, West Sussex RH13 8RA
by Cox & Wyman Ltd, Reading

ISBN 1 85304 030 4

© 1978 United Feature Syndicate, Inc.

© 1978 United Feature Syndicate, Inc.

FOR OUR LAST NIGHT OUT I'VE PLANNED SOMETHING SPECIAL

HOW ABOUT A MARSHMALLOW ROAST?

2-11

I'LL BUILD THE FIRE...YOU GET YOURSELVES SOME NICE LONG STICKS...

© 1978 United Feature Syndicate, Inc.

ALL RIGHT, TROOPS, HERE WE GO ON OUR SPRING HIKE...

4-24   © 1979 United Feature Syndicate, Inc.

REMEMBER, WE'RE OUT TO OBSERVE THE BEAUTY OF NATURE SO LET'S WATCH FOR NEW PLANTS, AND FLOWERS AND TREES...

AND CHICKS?

HEE HEE
HEE HEE
HEE HEE

© 1986 United Feature Syndicate, Inc.

8-9

© 1979 United Feature Syndicate, Inc.   8-13

"NEEDLES, CALIFORNIA..
A RECREATIONAL CENTER
ON THE COLORADO RIVER"

"ELEVATION, 463 FEET...
AVERAGE RAINFALL, FIVE
INCHES PER YEAR..."

8-15

"ATTRACTIONS IN THE
AREA ARE OLD GHOST
TOWNS AND TOPOCK SWAMP"

THAT MUST BE WHERE
MY BROTHER SPIKE
LIVES...TOPOCK SWAMP!

REALLY? WELL, I'M GLAD YOU ENJOYED THE HIKE, HARRIET....IT WAS NICE HAVING YOU WITH US...

OH, NO, YOU DON'T HAVE TO DO THAT..

5-17

WELL, IF YOU INSIST...

© 1980 United Feature Syndicate, Inc.

NO SCOUT LEADER ALIVE CAN TURN DOWN AN ANGEL FOOD CAKE WITH SEVEN-MINUTE FROSTING!

SCHULZ

EACH ONE OF YOU WILL TAKE A TURN TONIGHT AT GUARD DUTY

10-22

BILL, YOU HAVE THE FIRST TWO HOURS

© 1980 United Feature Syndicate, Inc.

FIND A PLACE TO STAND WHERE YOU COULD SPOT ANY INTRUDERS...

YES, SIR, I UNDERSTAND..

ONE OF SNOOPY'S BEAGLE SCOUTS GOT THROWN IN JAIL..I HAVE TO GO DOWN, AND GET HER OUT...

THAT STUPID DOG IS MORE TROUBLE THAN HE'S WORTH!

10-30

MOST OF US ARE

SPEAK FOR YOURSELF!

IN CASE YOU'RE WONDERING, HARRIET IS ALL RIGHT..THE ROUND-HEADED KID IS GOING TO BAIL HER OUT...

© 1980 United Feature Syndicate, Inc.

SO YOU SAY YOU WERE IN THIS PLACE CALLED "THE BIRDBATH" DRINKING ROOT BEER WHEN THESE BLUE JAYS CAME IN...

10-31

THEY STARTED TO GET INSULTING, AND THAT'S WHEN IT HAPPENED, HUH? THAT'S WHEN SHE DID IT?

THAT'S WHEN HARRIET HIT THE BLUE JAY IN THE FACE WITH THE ANGEL FOOD CAKE!

© 1981 United Feature Syndicate, Inc.

6-11

6-13

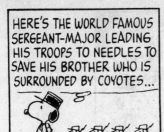

HERE'S THE WORLD FAMOUS SERGEANT-MAJOR LEADING HIS TROOPS TO NEEDLES TO SAVE HIS BROTHER WHO IS SURROUNDED BY COYOTES...

WE'LL HAVE TO HURRY, MEN! WE DON'T KNOW HOW LONG POOR SPIKE CAN HOLD OUT...

SPIKE WON'T GIVE UP WITHOUT A FIGHT, THOUGH.. HE'LL TAKE WHATEVER THEY THROW AT HIM!

2-23

NO FAIR SHOOTING RUBBER BANDS!

© 1983 United Feature Syndicate, Inc.

SCHULZ

OKAY, MEN, MOVE OUT! WE HAVE A LONG WAY TO GO, BUT SPIKE NEEDS OUR HELP!

I WONDER HOW HE'S DOING OUT THERE IN THE DESERT ALL ALONE FIGHTING OFF THE COYOTES

2-25   © 1983 United Feature Syndicate, Inc.

FORTUNATELY, SPIKE IS A REAL FIGHTER... HE KNOWS ALL THE TRICKS..

OW!

RATS! IT'S HARD TO SHOOT A RUBBER BAND WITHOUT HITTING YOUR OWN FINGERS!

THERE IT IS, MEN..
THE FANTASTIC LITTLE
TOWN OF NEEDLES!

AND SOMEWHERE OUT THERE
IN THE DESERT, MY
BROTHER, SPIKE, IS
SURROUNDED BY COYOTES...
WE HAVE TO RESCUE HIM!

2-28

ALL RIGHT, I NEED
ONE VOLUNTEER TO ACT
AS SCOUT...

© 1983 United Feature Syndicate, Inc

NO, YOU CAN'T
VOLUNTEER
HARRIET BECAUSE
SHE ISN'T HERE

SCHULZ

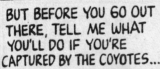

BEFORE WE LEAVE, SPIKE, TELL ME WHY THE COYOTES WERE SO MAD AT YOU...

SPIKE'S REAL ESTATE

"OCEAN VIEW CONDOMINIUMS FOR SALE, CHEAP"

YOU TRIED TO SELL OCEAN VIEW CONDOMINIUMS IN THE MIDDLE OF THE DESERT?

3-10

I FIGURED THAT COYOTES COULD SEE A LONG WAY

© 1983 United Feature Syndicate Inc

CAN YOU IMAGINE THAT? WE MARCH ALL THE WAY OUT HERE TO RESCUE MY BROTHER FROM THE COYOTES, AND YOU KNOW WHY?

ALL BECAUSE OF SOME REAL ESTATE DEAL... HOW CAN YOU SELL CONDOMINIUMS TO A BUNCH OF COYOTES?

3-11

© 1983 United Feature Syndicate, Inc.

ANYWAY, MEN, YOU DID A GOOD JOB, AND WHEN WE GET BACK, I'LL PUT YOU IN FOR A UNIT CITATION AND A THREE-DAY PASS...

NO, OLIVIER, YOU'D NEVER MAKE IT TO PARIS ON A THREE-DAY PASS

NOW, REMEMBER, WE HAVEN'T COME ALL THE WAY TO "POINT LOBOS" JUST TO TAKE VACATION PICTURES!

I WANT EACH OF YOU TO LOOK AROUND FOR POSSIBLE PHOTOGRAPHS THAT MAY HAVE REAL...

© 1983 United Feature Syndicate, Inc. 6-24

CLICK!

..ARTISTIC QUALITY!

KNOWING WHAT TO BRING ON A HIKE IS VERY IMPORTANT..

FOOD AND WATER, OF COURSE, ARE ALWAYS A NECESSITY..MAYBE A COMPASS...

6-1

KNOWING WHAT TO LEAVE BEHIND CAN ALSO BE IMPORTANT...

WHAT I'M SAYING, CONRAD, IS THAT IT WAS NOT NECESSARY TO BRING A SUNDIAL!

Other Snoopy titles published by Ravette Books

Black and white landscapes

It's a Dog's Life	£2.50
Roundup	£2.50
Freewheelin'	£2.50
Joe Cool	£2.50
Chariots For Hire	£2.50
Dogs Don't Eat Dessert	£2.50
You're on the Wrong Foot Again, Charlie Brown	£2.50
By Supper Possessed	£2.95

Weekenders

No. 1 Weekender	£4.95

All these books are available at your local bookshop or news-agent, or can be ordered direct from the publisher. Just tick the titles you require and fill in the form below. Prices and availability subject to change without notice.

Ravette Books Limited, 3 Glenside Estate, Star Road, Partridge Green, Horsham, West Sussex RH13 8RA

Please send a cheque or postal order, and allow the following for postage and packing. UK: Snoopy Stars – 45p for one book, 20p for a second book and 15p for each additional book. Other titles – 50p for one book and 30p for each additional book.

Name ....

Address ....

....